The Spyventures of Cloudy & Rosie

Cloudy & Rosie

A SPY AND HIS SPY-ASSISTANT-IN-TRAINING

The Spyventures of Cloudy & Rosie
Irene van Raadshooven

Published 2020 by Irene van Raadshooven

ISBN: 978-90-9033652-7

Contact: info@littlebelle.org

I dedicate this book to our Cloudy & Rosie,
to all the other dogs in our family - on earth and in heaven -
and to dogs everywhere around the world.

You all bring joy, happiness, love, and so much magic
to our lives and to the world.

Introduction

Dear Cloudy,

Once, you wandered on remote, rural roads in Spain. Nobody saw you, nor your pain, nor how you suffered because of a severe infection in your mouth. Due to the infection, your nose got crooked and your lower jawbone was gone. You must also have been in pain when walking because your pelvis was completely broken on both sides. It's still completely loose and the two halves will never grow back together again. How did you feel, all alone? One day, someone saw you and saved you. This was the start of a completely new chapter in your life. Not long after you were rescued, I found you. Or did you find me?

From being timid and cautious, you started to feel more confident every day. Your smile came through and didn't leave your face. I saw you, the real you, once you realized you were truly loved. For who you are. You opened your heart.

Your intense joy, curiosity, and sense of adventure are contagious. The way you face life, explore the world, and your passion remind me of our angel Little Belle, who had the same intense curiosity and zest for life.

You make me smile a lot, little man. You taught me, and still teach me, how to live every day without Belle physically by my side. You will never be alone again. Whatever crosses your path, we will always face it together. See how even in this picture our angel in heaven shines her ray of light on you?

I'm by your side. Always and forever.
I love you, little man, I love you more than words can ever say ♥

~ Your mom Irene

SimplyDog

Dear Rosie,

The first ten years of your life, spending day after day imprisoned in a puppy mill, were horrible. Your only purpose was to give birth to as many puppies as possible. Your little ones weren't really ever yours, and were taken from you much too soon. I know that your only wish was for them to be happy. No one can ever take away a mother's love.

One day you were rescued. What did you feel the moment you were freed from your cage? I can imagine it must have been strange to find out that the world is much bigger than the tiny world you lived in for all those years. It must also have been strange to learn that there are humans who do have true compassion.

The first picture I saw of you was the one taken when you had just been rescued. I was saddened by the look of despair on your face, and deeply touched by the look of complete innocence. I saw such a beautiful and gentle soul.

When I saw you for the first time in real life, you were so much tinier than I had thought. I lifted you in my arms and almost couldn't feel your weight. Immediately, you relaxed, breathed out, and put your little head in that special place between my neck and shoulder, the spot you still love so much. Finally home. Finally loved.

You got to know your big family, all your brothers and sisters, and now you love to take naps and to go on many adventures together with them. From very timid and shy, you changed into a little girl with big eyes looking out into the world with so much more confidence and pure joy. Even when you are in dreamland, you have this enchanting smile on your face.
From the beginning, you were fascinated by your adventurous brother Cloudy, and started to follow him everywhere. That's when the spyventures started...

I love you so much, my little girl. You are my everything ♥
~ Your mom Irene

Hi, I am Cloudy,
a.k.a.
Cloud007

Hi, I am Rosie,
a.k.a.
spy-assistant-in-training

Together we will share pictures and stories of our daily life and, of course, of our spyventures!

My spy master says we can't go
outside for our secret missions.
It's raining nonstop and spies
can't get wet and cold...
Cloudnificent advice:
always stay dry and warm!

Sometimes a spy also
needs a blanket...

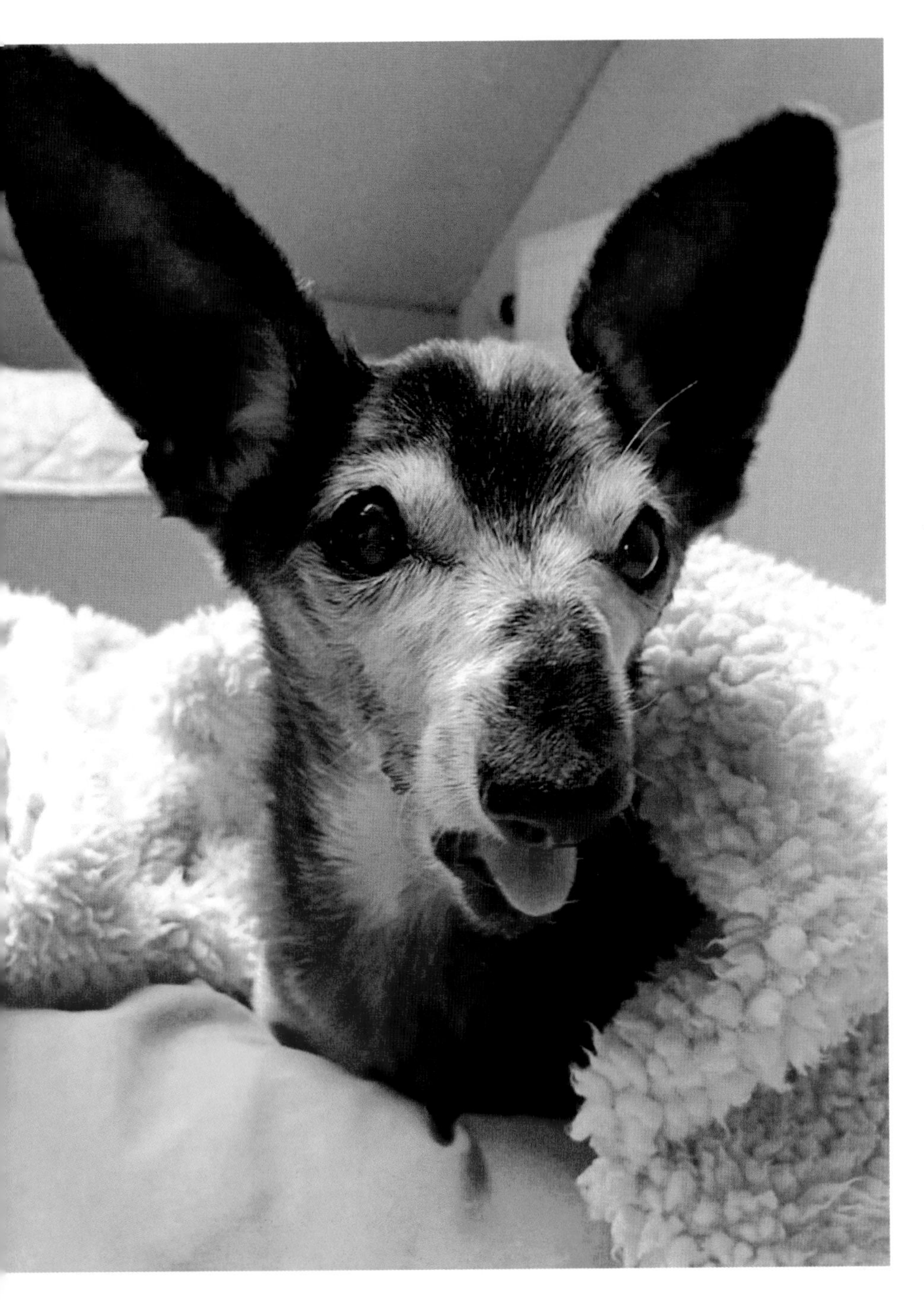

Wait a minute, I hear
something!
Yeah, my cloudnificent
ears don't miss
anything important,
especially when it's
related to food.
Dinner is ready!
Bye!

Of course, being the best spy ever, I also have the best spy tongue ever. That's why I can eat my food so well!
It's a secret, but well, because you are my best friends ever, I thought I could share this with you.
But remember, for your eyes only.

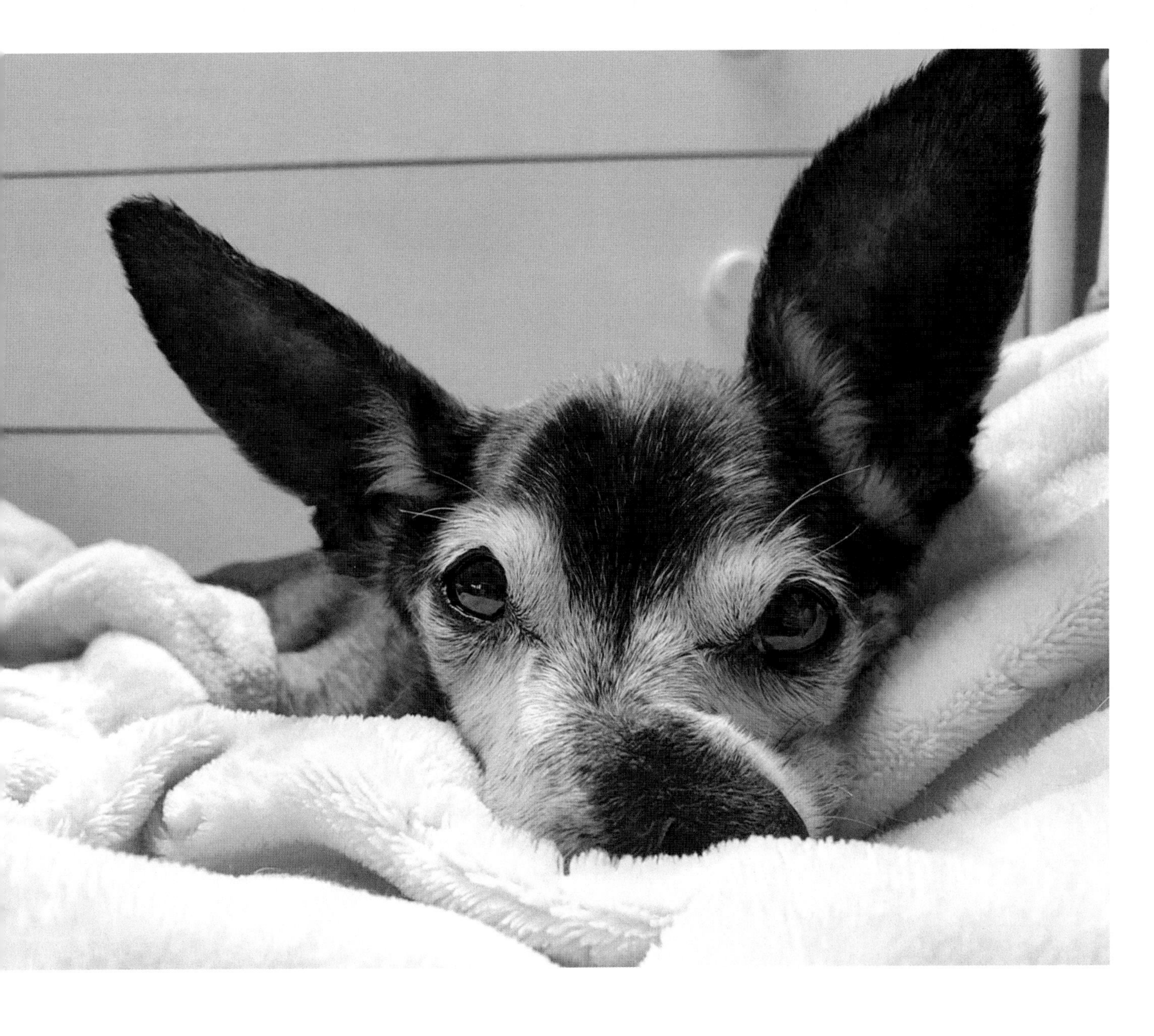

Oh, oh, oh! What can a spy do on a rainy day, again?
(a spy who doesn't like rain, ever)

What can we do while
it's raining?
Well, I showed spy master
a new trick I have
invented all by myself!
I called it the
'Strange Rosie Angle',
a trick that's perfect
during an
undercover operation.

Cloud007 was
pretty impressed.
'Cool!' he said.
He added only that my
name in the middle would
reveal who I am. Oh, yes,
he's so smart!

I'm still learning.

We're going on a mission...
On our way there, we'll discuss whether we can
share it with you or whether it must stay a secret.

Okay, we can tell you!
We're on a mission in
a pet shop!

'Rosie, look at me.'
Then I show her how
to examine all the
delicious smelling
treats.

'Always step into the
box, Rosie. Always.'

While doing some
grocery shopping,
suddenly encounter a horse
ıat looks quite different from
my horse family at home.

)f course, a spy like me finds
this suspicious so I'm
checking to make sure
he is okay.

I think we're friends now.

I don't like rain. I don't like water.
I don't like big puddles of water, nor the little ones.
I don't like getting wet. I don't like getting cold.
So, smart as I am, I created my own warm and cozy spot,
and decided to stay here all day long.
Yes, besides being cloudnificent, I am also spytelligent.

Okay, okay, I will show myself for a moment.
I know you love to see my handsome face at least once a day, right?

Hi!
I wish you all a happy and beautiful day!

Wait, I have to show you both sides of my pretty face!

During my secret undercover missions, I'm soooo good at hiding!
That's why I am the best spy ever.

Sssttt...
Benji doesn't know that
I'm following her.

That's what spies do...

As you all know, I'm teaching Rosie some very important spy stuff, and today's lesson is about how to spy watch your surroundings.

Okay, yes, I've seen it all.
Everything is safe!
I am going
back inside again.

A spy needs warmth.

Hi, we have just been outside. It was really cold, so we just went to the stables for... well, you know. To feel nice and warm again, I have taught Rosie to sit close to the warm radiator. I'm very good at teaching important life - uhm - spy lessons.

This is a spy-yawn. It's a secret code.
In the last picture I asked Rosie if she understood.
She said it looked silly, not having a clue about my message.
That's why she's still a spy-assistant-in-training.

Hi!
I wanted to 'give' you
some nice snowdrops
because I love you!
Then I stepped on them.
Well, it's all about the good
spy-intention.

By the way,
I was busy investigating
the fallen tree behind me.
Safety first!

I wonder when my
dinner will be ready?

Ohhh, waiting for dinner does
make me feel sleepy...

'Have we arrived, Cloudy?'

'Yes, Rosie, I recognize this place from 2 weeks ago.'

'Okay, let's go!'

'It's beautiful here,
spy master!'

'It is, Rosie. It's an amazing
spyventure.'

'Always follow
your nose, Rosie.'

'Rosie?'

'Yes, spy master?'

'We've just arrived hom
Now listen to me very
carefully: remember th
special look I taught yo
the one that helps us
to get our dinner fast?

'Oh, yes! I will give mon
Irene THAT look.
I'm very hungry!'

'Rosie, you're a
cloudnificent student.

A rainy day means a
spy napping day.

Even when I am
in dreamland,
I just know when
a picture is being taken,
so I give THE eye.

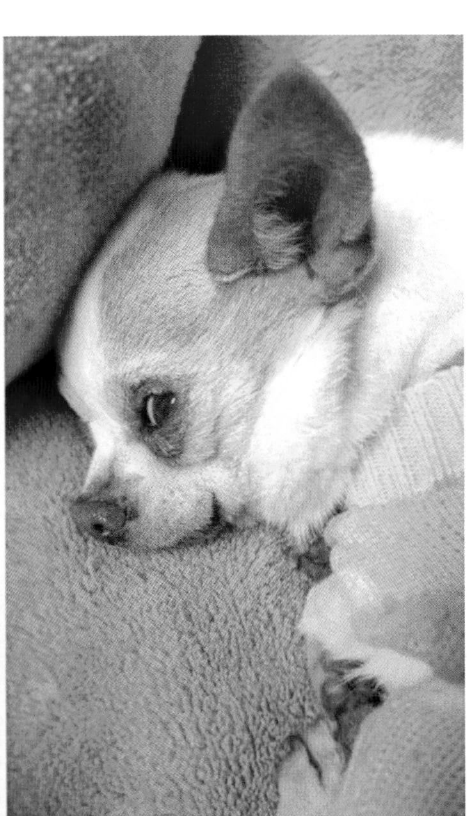

Just exploring.
No rain today, but it's still cold
so I think I will go
inside soon again.
A cold spy isn't a good spy.

I have to agree with spy master:
it's pretty ccccold.
A shivering spy-assistant-in-training
isn't a good spy-assistant-in-training.
Cloud007 has taught me well.
I'm going inside now. Bye!

I found a beautiful flower and decided that
it's my gift to you, to make you smile.

Because it's been
raining a lot,
I thought it would be a
cloudnificent idea to
investigate our house.

Somehow, I caught
something on my nose.
It might seem a tiny
detail, but for a spy it
could be a BIG clue!

It’s very nice you take a picture of the best spy ever, but I'm verrry hungry!
I know that last night we moved the clocks back one hour,
so you have to think about that.
Oh, it's good you have me, the most intelligent spy ever,
so I can remind you of this important matter.

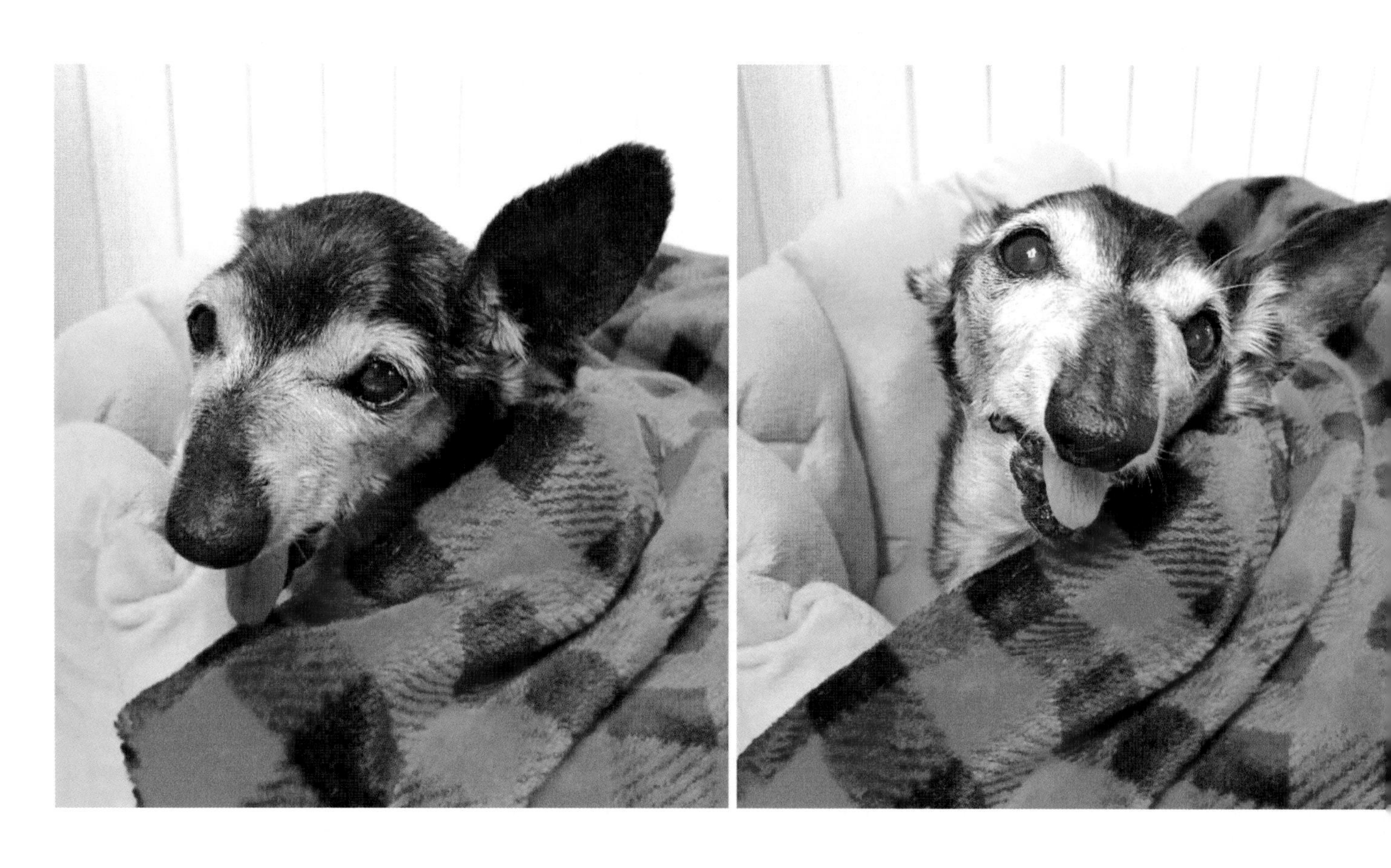

It's cold today, so for the first time in months we had to put the heater on again. And mom Irene put a blanket on me.
I like it. A spy needs warmth.

Where are we going today?

Oh... where are we?
There is a beautiful
big lake here.
A great place for
spyventures!

I don't need to wear
a sweater, only my
red spy cape.

‘Okay, spy-assistant-in-training Rosie,
tell me: have we arrived home? Otherwise, I will continue my spy nap.'

'I am looking at Irene,
as you taught me,
spy master,
and yes,
by the look on her face
I can tell we've arrived home!'

'Excellent spy job, Rosie!’

Sssttt... it's me. I'm undercover and just needed to check. That's what spies do. Bye!

Hey, you can't take a picture of us while we're in the middle of an important meeting discussing our next secret mission!

Here is my extra-special
incognito spy move,
this time combined
with my paw!

Rosie wants to learn how
to do it, too, but so far,
she hasn't been able to
perform this move.

That's okay -
only the best spy
in the world has this
unique skill.

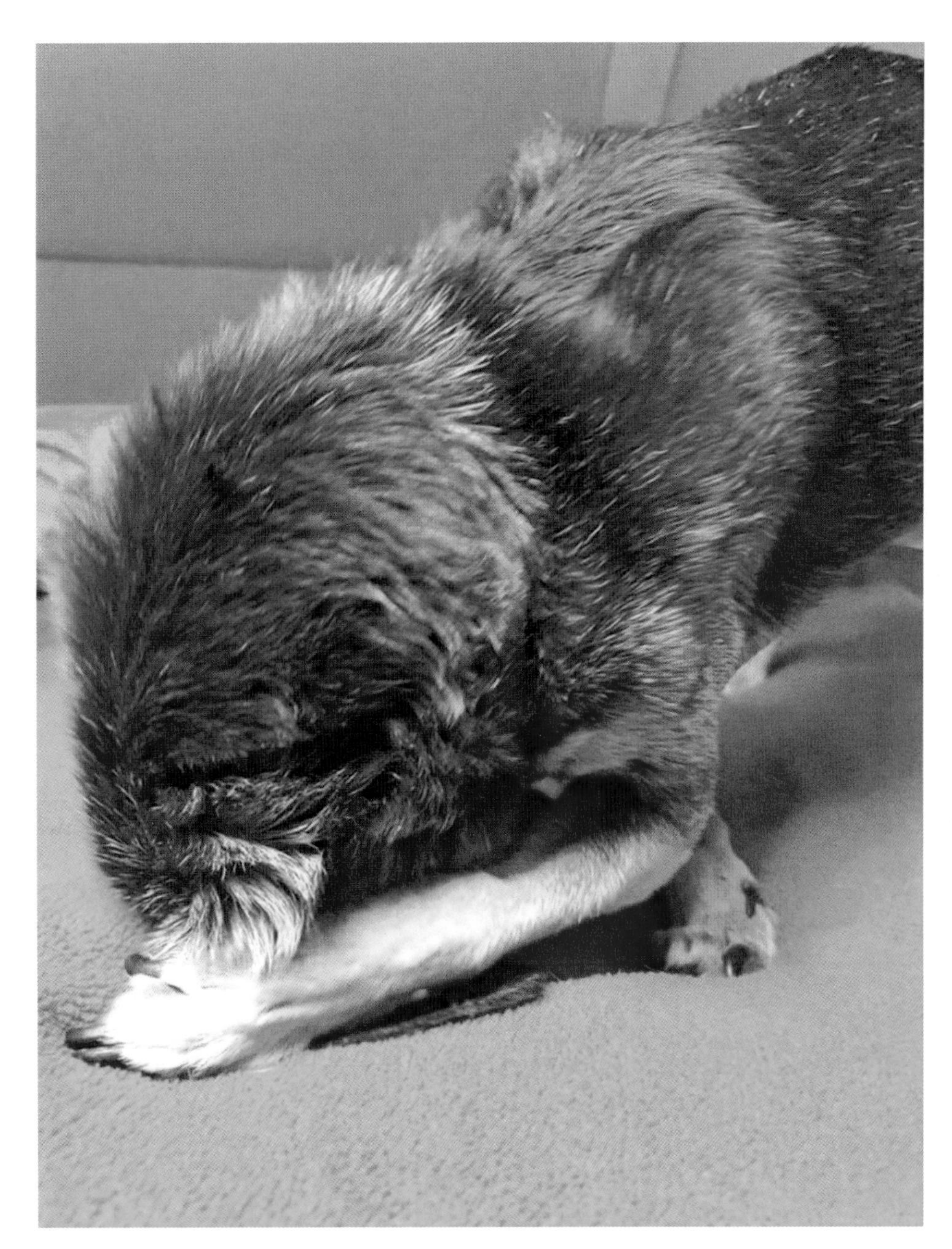

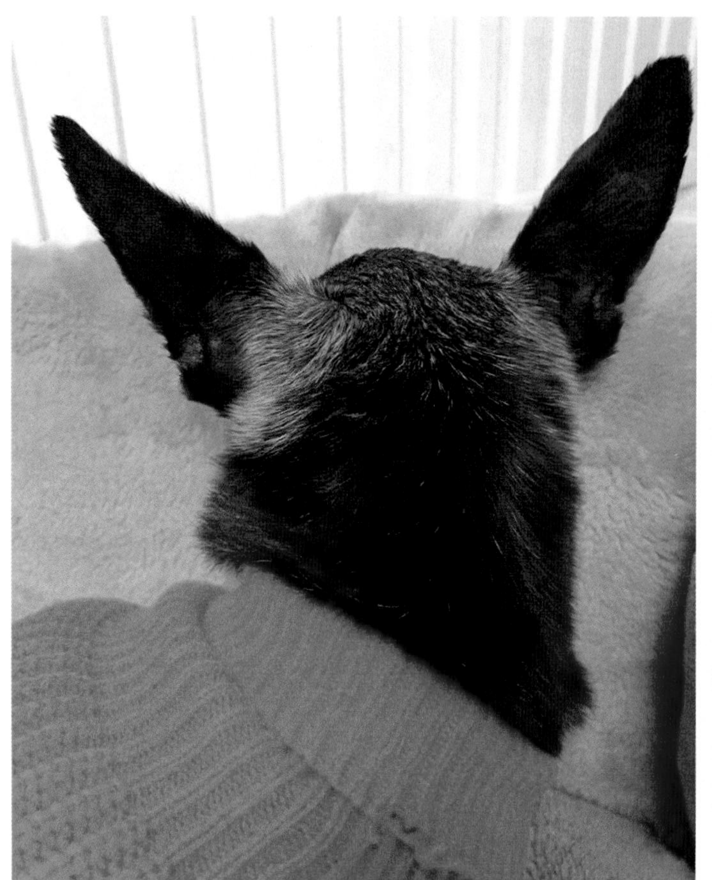

Sorry. Secret spy adventures
in dreamland, so
I can't reveal myself.

Okay, okay, it's me!
I'm so funny that I have to laugh at my own jokes. Of course, the best spy ever also knows the best jokes ever.

‘What are we going to do today, spy master?'

'Nothing in particular, little Rosie; we're just going to enjoy the lights.'

'Oh, you're very smart. I love the lights.'

'I always have cloudnificent ideas, Rosie.'

I love my little Christmas house.
After spending the first ten years of my life in a puppy mill, this is my first Christmas in a home and with my family, who love me so much.
Just magical!

Of course, after dinner (which is my number one priority), I also had to investigate the little Christmas house. Rosie was right:
it's a magical place.
Spies love magic, too.

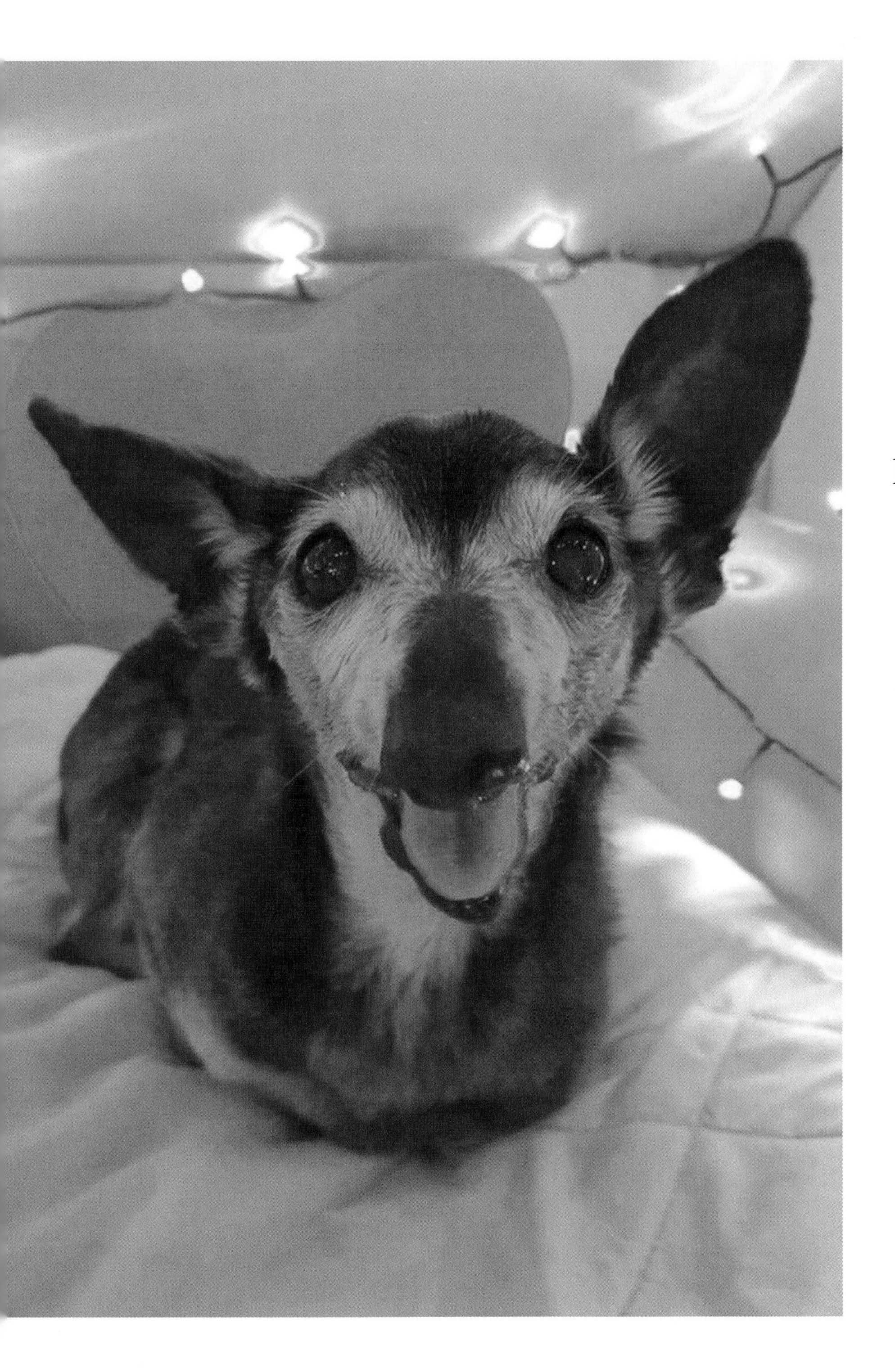

You might think I'm a
lazy spy because I sleep
all day long,
but a smart spy knows
when to act and
when it's better to rest.
All winter long
I spybernate.

That's why I'm the
smartest spy ever.

My spy master told me that
we can't get outside today
because it's grey and
very ccccold.
When it's this cold I often
shiver, and he explained
that spy work
and trembling aren't a
great combination for
secret missions.

Cloud007 always gives
cloudnificent advice.

A spy selfie!

Is it at least 20 degrees Celcius outside?
No?
Then I'm not going. Just wake me up
when summer has arrived.

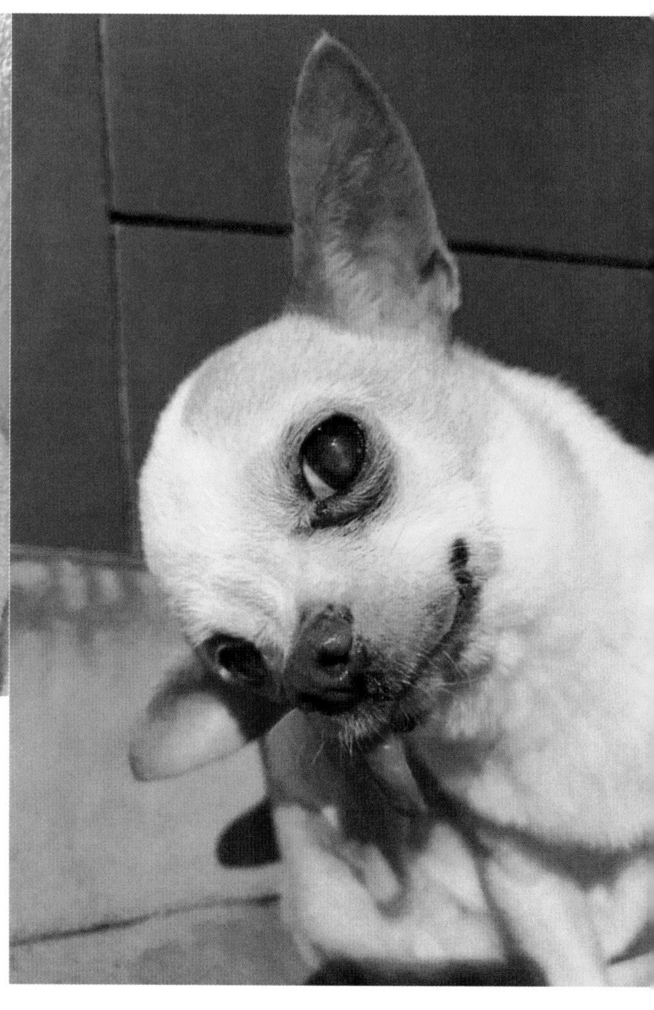

Just scratching my ear...
Sometimes you just gotta do
what you gotta do.

We've just picked up
some medicines at the
animal clinic, and now
I will drive us home!

A spy like me has
many talents.

I think my spy master
can drive cloudnificently!
We've arrived home safe
and well.
During our ride I looked
at him like this,
full of admiration.
He's the best spy ever!

P.s. Cloud007 told me
he will teach me
how to drive, too,
although he said it
will be quite a
challenge because
I am soooo tiny.

I was telling Emi a spy story and she listened with interest.
Then I asked, ‘What shall we do today?’ and she just fell asleep...

The weather is pretty
cold with a chilly wind
but luckily, I can enjoy
the sunshine
from inside
- on my spy throne.

Picture top left: 'Hey, are you there?'
Bottom left: 'I see you!'
Right: 'Ah, great spot to watch you forever. Love you!'

Look how big my nose is! Yes, I have an extraordinary, or better said, cloudnificent, keen sense of smell. That's why I'm the best spy ever!

‘Okay, Rosie, we've arrived.’

‘Are you sure, Cloudy?’

‘Of course, little one. My spy radar works cloudnificently.’

Wow, lots of paint stuff
over here! A great place for a
thorough spy-inspection.

Rosie isn't a great help with
the spy-inspection.
At the moment, she prefers to
be a sleepy princess instead
of a spy-assistant-in-training.

On our way home, Cloud007 gave me the task to stay alert and watch our surroundings, so he could take a spy nap.
Of course, that's what friends, uhm spy-assistants-in-training, are for...

Red spy cape: - Check!
Purple spy protection coat
- Check!

Spy ready for cold,
wet weather:
- No way!

Don't worry.
I know that someone is watching me.
My spy detection radar works 360 degrees.
It's a spy gift. Just stay calm.
I have everything under control.

I have the feeling that someone
is watching me, too...
What to do, spy master?

Just show him your butt, Rosie.
This will teach him a valuable lesson:
never to mess with a spy or
his spy-assistant-in-training.

I'm trying your tactic, spy master,
and I think it works!
You're a cloudnificent teacher and I'm a
cloudnificent spy-assistant-in-training
The best spy team ever!

I'm on a secret mission,
so I need to hide my big ears.
This way no one will recognize me.

Okay, okay, it's me.
Surprise!

I just had a wonderful adventure exploring the stables with my siblings.
Now I'm a bit tired, so I will take a nice nap before dinner.
Or maybe I'll first have dinner and then I'll take a long evening nap.
Hmm, yes, this sounds a lot better!

Cute spy

Tough spy

Just kidding, I was just playing!

I thought it would be nice to bring you some sunshine and flowers.
I hope they will give you a smile.

Yesterday,
there was sunshine,
but now the sun has
just dissapeared
and there is a cold wind.
I told mom Irene
to just keep
my sweater like this.
A spy can never ever
have cold ears!

And, I think I look
cloudnificently handsome,
don't I?

I don't understand why this stuffed friend is suspicious.

I kinda like him.

Spy master told me that's why I'm still his spy-assistant-in-training.

I haven't done a lot today.
It was too cold, and my spy nose needed rest, too.

Of course, a spy needs to
check the hay bales too!
First, I make sure my
surroundings are safe,
then I do my special
spy move.

You did smile, didn't you?
I am sooo funny,
I must be the funniest spy ever!

Abort mission!
Abort mission!

I see a cookie!

I can't be a big brother
like Cloudy,
but I can be a princess.

Okay, a big brother
and a princess together.

Did you know that my ears are so special that they don't always fit in a picture?
I'm the only spy with such big ears. That's why I'm the best spy ever.

Oh, and one more thing: don't think that my big ears will blow my cover.
When I need to, I can make my ears look smaller, and...
I can hide my tongue! See?

No one will ever recognize me.

Today, I am supervising Jessie's birthday digging
party to make sure everything is safe.
Yes, even on birthdays, a spy needs to stay alert.

After a thorough spyvestigation, I have found out that when it looks like beautiful and warm weather looking out a window, this can be very misleading. I had to wear my sweater, then asked for an extra coat, too, and then I felt the wet grass beneath my paws. Fortunately, my spy wisdom led me to this conclusion, so next time I know it's best to just continue my spy naps with the sun's rays beaming on me through the window.

Normally, this knowledge would be a secret,
but I love you, so I am sharing it with you this time.

See, even inside, I can catch the sunlight!
It's my spy magic.

Okay, listen to me. My spy master told me that the clock has sprung forward an hour (he really knows everything). He told me to think about this very carefully, especially as it relates to dinner. And now I know this means that we get dinner one hour earlier! Okay, where is it?

My spy-assistant-in-
training, Rosie,
did a cloudnificent job!
We had a delicious
dinner, and now it's
time for a
nice evening nap.

A spy hug for all my
beautiful friends
around the world ❤

'Just watch what I'm doing, spy-assistant-in-training;
this is very important spy stuff.'
'I've no clue what you're doing, spy master. It looks pretty odd.'
'Oh... you will learn eventually, Rosie
- maybe after a few more years of spy-training.'

A spy always knows where
to find the best spots!
From this bench I have a
cloudnificent view of my
surroundings.

Yes, that piece of
bread is for me!
It's very little, though.
I would love to have the
rest of your sandwich, too.

I fit quite perfectly in Rosie's little bed.
Of course, a spy like me
fits in everywhere.

Okay, my spy master fits in my little bed,
and I fit well in this big bed.
Isn't that amazing?!
As a spy-assistant-in-training
I can do some spy magic, too.

Spy-assistant-in-training is
not available for spy duty.
I'm sorry, spy master.

That's okay, Rosie, I'm not available
for secret missions, either,
although my ears always stay alert.

I was investigating the hay
- part of my job -
when I found these feathers.
As I was sniffing them,
one got stuck on my head!
Very suspicious!

Luckily, I know a
very good tactic:
one famous spy sneeze,
and it was gone.

I'm also on a spy missior
in the stables, and I have
found lots of clues.
Oh, and I just made
this bubble.
Isn't it amazing?!

My spy master
didn't teach me this,
it's my own magical
spy trick.

Sssst, I'm hiding in the high grass.
Cloudnificent cover, isn't it?

Look how beautiful this cherry
blossom tree is blooming!
The flowers smell so
nice and sweet.

I can show you the whole cherry
blossom tree in a spytastic way!
I'm so clever.
And handsome, of course.

Yes, those soft cookies are for me!
I can't eat hard treats.
Well, a smart spy like me knows
that soft cookies are the most
delicious anyway.

Rosie has a great technique, too,
to show how much she loves cookies.
I didn't know that her tongue was that big!

We're a perfect spy team.

Hi! What shall we do today?
I think we will just enjoy
the beautiful sunshine,
and I will take as many
spy naps as possible.

Doesn't this sound
cloudnificent?!

I love the sunshine, the flowers, the blue sky, and...

Oh, and you!

We're ready for a new spyventure!

While I am keeping an eye
on our surroundings,
spy-assistant-in-training
Rosie is practicing her side-eye.

This is how a princess,
- oh I mean a
spy-princess -
loves to enjoy
the sunshine.

I found a cloudnificent
hiding place!
It smells pretty
nice over here.
Spring has arrived,
and nature is blooming.
Isn't that wonderful?
When sensing nature's
magic around me,
I feel extra strength and
hope within me.
Always keep hope alive
in your heart,
my friends ❤

Yes, I also love nature,
but I have an
important question:
isn't it dinner time already?
Spy-assistants-in-training
need lots of food, too.
Spy missions require
a lot of energy.
My spy master told me so.

It's raining again.
My spy master says
that spies are not
allowed to get wet,
so I assume this rule
also applies for
spy-assistants-in-training.
I'm not going
outside today.

Love you ❤

'Rosie?' 'Yes, spy master?'

'You forgot to tell everyone something very important.' 'Oh, what is it?'

'That we have a very, VERY special birthday on Wednesday.'

'I thought that was a secret?'

'We won't reveal yet whose birthday it is, Rosie,

only that it's someone very VERY special!'

'I wonder if people couldn't guess by now who it is...'

Okay, okay, I can reveal
THE secret:
it's MY birthday
tomorrow!
Oh, it will be so special,
especially for you
because you've probably
never celebrated a
spy's birthday before.

Happy birthday to me!
Happy birthday to me!
Happy birthday,
ost handsome spy ever...
Happy birthday to me!

I was singing,
so I look pretty funny.
Well, I am always very
funny anyway.

What are you
waiting for?
That's a spy cookie!
Mine!
For my birthday I can
have as many cookies
as I want.

A secret spy move,
especially for you,
to thank you for all
the amazing happy
birthday wishes!
They make my
spy heart
very happy.

My spy master is teaching me
how to say the secret spy code
so the gate will open.
I think I deserve an A+.

First, Rosie, you must always
check to be sure if it's safe to
approach the gate.

Like this.

Okay, I think I can do this, spy master.

Yes, closer, Rosie...

Like this, spy master?

Yes, Rosie, that's cloudnificent!
Okay, we can't share the rest of the lesson with everyone, as the spy-code is top secret...

'Good spy job, Rosie!
You keep an eye on
that side, and I will
cover the rest of our
surroundings.'
Rosie winks...

My nose needs rest.
One ear does not.
Once a spy, always a spy.

A while ago I had a very
interesting spy lesson.
Spy master told me
all about
THE look.
So, I am trying it today.
I'm on mom Irene's lap
and here is my
'THE LOOK'.
Now she says,
'Oh, Rosie, do you think
it's time for dinner?'
I'm getting better
and better
at this spy stuff.

'Look, Rosie,
this is how you
do the spy move!'

When you drive past beautiful tulips, but you can't visit the field,
you just have to find another way to look at them.
A spy like me always has cloudnificent solutions.

Look! I found a tulip field
that we can visit up close.
It's so beautiful!

It's beautiful indeed, although you
can't see much of the tulips
because of my big ears.
Sorry, it's a spy thing.

Look how smart I am!
This time, I am making sure that my ears are in
the right position so you can still see the tulips.

I tried to do the trick that my spy master did the last time:
hiding the tulips with my ears.
It's not so easy! You can still see where I am, right?

Pure spy bliss!

Thank you for following our spyventures!
We hope that we made you smile 😊 ❤

Little Belle

ABOUT CLOUDY'S AND ROSIE'S FAMILY

One day, a little dog named Little Belle changed our lives. After she passed away in 2017, in her memory, we established Little Belle's Magical Sanctuary, where we give a forever home to old(er) and differently abled dogs.
Soon, a book about Little Belle's life will be published. Till then, you can find her inspirational story on www.littlebelle.org, where you can also read Cloudy's and Rosie's story along with the other dogs' stories.

www.littlebellesmagicalsanctuary.org

You can follow our daily pictures and stories on our Facebook page:
www.facebook.com/LittleBelleDog
And Instagram: www.instagram.com/littlebelle1

Made in the USA
Coppell, TX
20 January 2021